Scale Time!

A step-by-step approach to
Scales, Arpeggios and Broken Chords

Piano, Grade 1

DAVID TURNBULL

CONTENTS

Bosworth

i

To the Teacher

Scales are essential to the development of fluent piano technique. Without a knowledge of scales, and a facility in their execution, no progress is possible. This is equally true of arpeggios and broken chords.

Nevertheless, some pupils are reluctant to learn and practise scales as they should. Many teachers have found it difficult to persuade pupils to work as hard at scales as at pieces. Many examiners could bear witness to the inadequate knowledge of scales shown by some candidates.

It is hoped that the step-by-step approach in this book towards the learning of Grade 1 Scales will help pupils to practise the technical requirements of the syllabus more easily, and provide greater enjoyment. Anything done well will give pleasure, just as anything done half-heartedly is boring, and this is as true of scales as of anything else.

Alternative fingerings. In examinations, any systematic fingering which works is acceptable. Sometimes, scale manuals suggest alternative fingerings, but it is the author's view that those printed here are the best for almost all pupils. Teachers will of course use their own discretion in this matter.

Some preliminary finger exercises are printed on page iii which may be helpful, especially for the turning of the thumb. I am grateful to my wife for preparing these exercises, and for much other advice and help. I am most grateful also to Paul Terry at Musonix for a number of suggestions, as well as for the care and skill with which he has done the typesetting.

David Turnbull
Solihull, England, 1997

Other material by David Turnbull published by Bosworth and Co.

Scale Time!   Piano Grade 2. Other books in this series in preparation.

Starting to Sight Read, Piano Grade 1, Piano Grade 2.

Aural Time!   Grades 1–8 (separate volumes for each grade)
Pupils' books for *Aural Time!* Grades 4 and 5, 6, 7, 8.
Compact Discs for *Aural Time!* Grades 6 and 7.
Easy Sight Singing Practice for Aural Tests and Singing Examinations.

Theory Time! Grades 1–5 (separate volumes for each grade).

To the Pupil

1   Scales, arpeggios and broken chords are a great help towards progress on the piano, and should be practised daily, and memorised.

   They will improve your sense of key, and give you greater ability to move about the keyboard. As they are really the building blocks of music, they will help you in understanding as well as in playing the notes the composer has written.

2   Make sure that you know what the notes are of the scale you are practising. At the beginning of each section there is a diagram showing you the notes to use. (See also the information on scales in *Theory Time!*).

3   The position of the hand and the movement of the fingers need care.

   WRIST POSITION. The wrist should be held so that if forms a continuous straight line with the lower arm. Don't let it drop.

   FINGER SHAPE. The fingers should be bent at both joints, so that the finger tips are almost in a straight line with each other.

   The keys should be played with the pads of the fingers – for this you must keep your nails short.

   Never allow the finger joints to become unbent.

   Raise the fingers from the knuckle joints before letting them descend to play each note.

   THE THUMB presses the key by using its side. It too should rise before it falls.

   When the thumb has to 'turn under' after fingers 3 or 4 have been used, make sure that it passes under the fingers smoothly, *without the wrist being raised*.

   When playing *ascending* right-hand scales, try to start moving the thumb to the right as finger 2 touches the key. In the same way, when playing *descending* left-hand scales, move the thumb to the left.

   Don't allow the thumb to play more loudly than the fingers.

Play the scales very slowly at first but always as rhythmically as you can. Play them more quickly only when they are absolutely safe. In examinations, the recommended *minimum* tempo for scales is 60 crotchets per minute, and for arpeggios and broken chords 45 dotted crotchets per minute. Your teacher may recommend that sometimes you use a metronome, setting a slow tempo at first and then increasing the speed. Whatever tempo is chosen, **rhythmic** playing is essential.

You will learn the scales in groups of fingers. However, when you play the whole scale you do so evenly and without accents – there should be no gaps between the finger groups.

Some finger exercises are printed on the next page, which may help you play evenly.

Preliminary Exercises

Practise these slowly, but very rhythmically, with each hand separately. Make sure that fingering is correct and that the notes are even in volume. Gradually increase the tempo as you become more confident.

The Scale of C major and Pattern 1 Fingering

1 The scale of C major uses white notes only, C – D – E – F – G – A – B and top C.

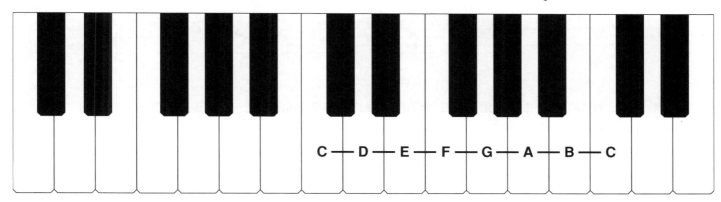

2 Play the RIGHT HAND of C major going up slowly and carefully.

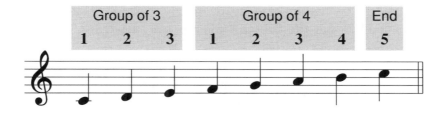

3 Play the scale of C major going up (ascending), then going down (descending).

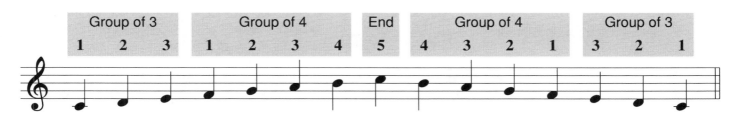

4 Notice and learn that
- first there is a **group of three notes**, fingered 1, 2 and 3
- then there is a **group of four notes** fingered 1, 2, 3 and 4
- then there is the **end note**, played with the little finger, 5
- when the scale is reversed, so is the finger pattern

This finger pattern, called Pattern 1, is used in *all* Grade 1 scales except the right hand of F major.

5 The finger pattern for the LEFT HAND is also Pattern 1. Play it going down first.

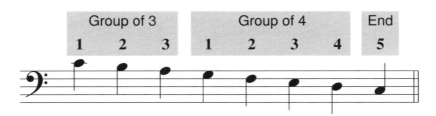

6   Play the scale of C major with the left hand, going down first, then up.

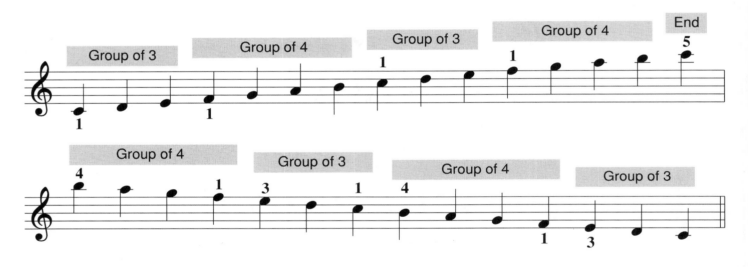

7   Practise the right hand and left hand one-octave scales frequently, until you can play them *from memory* accurately, evenly and rhythmically.

---

8   TO EXTEND A SCALE UP BY A SECOND OCTAVE, play the first group of three notes followed by the first group of four, then a second group of three followed by a second group of four, then the end note. The scale descends in reverse order.

Play the two-octave scale of C major going up in the right hand. Play it smoothly, in a steady tempo. It will help you if you remember that **the fourth finger is only used for B**.

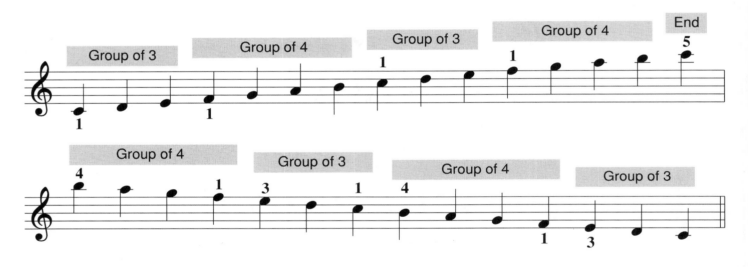

9   Play the two-octave scale of C major going down in the left hand, then up. Play it smoothly, in a steady tempo. It will help you if you remember that **the fourth finger is only used for D**.

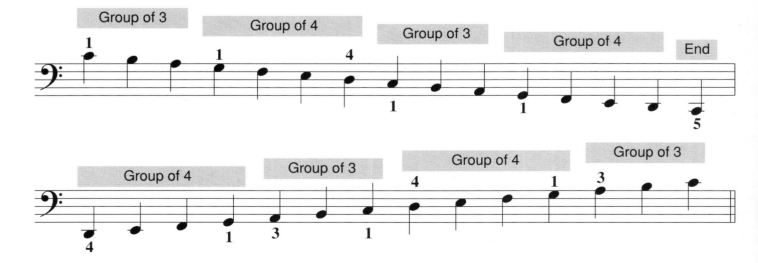

10 Once you can play the scale in **9** accurately, fluently and evenly, play it upwards first, then downwards.

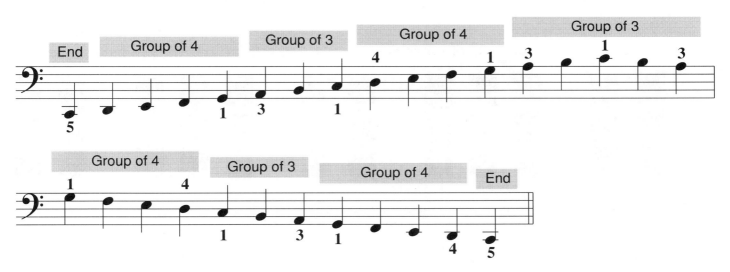

11 When you can play the scales steadily and evenly, try playing them more quickly. In examinations the notes are played as quavers in groups of four. Try to play at a speed of at least 60 crotchets per minute.

C major, right hand

C major, left hand

or

C major in contrary motion

You must also learn to play one octave of C major hands together, in contrary motion. The fingering is the same in both hands, and is shown between the staves. Play it slowly at first, increasing the tempo as you become more confident. Notice that on the first and last notes both thumbs play the same note.

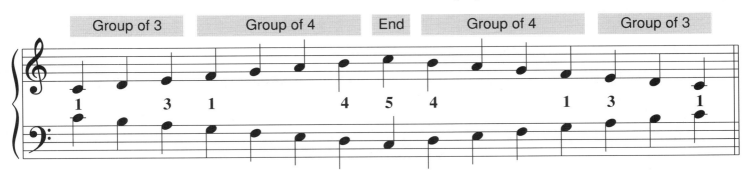

4

The Scale of G major

1 The scale of G major is made up of the notes G – A – B – C – D – E – F *sharp* and top G.

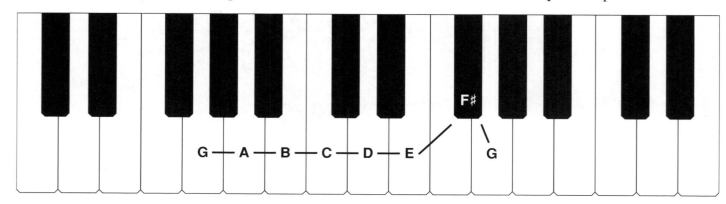

2 Pattern 1 fingering is also used for G major, but this time the pattern starts on the note G.

Play the RIGHT HAND of G major going up slowly and carefully.

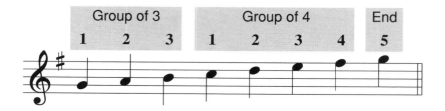

3 Play the right hand of the scale of G major going up, then down.

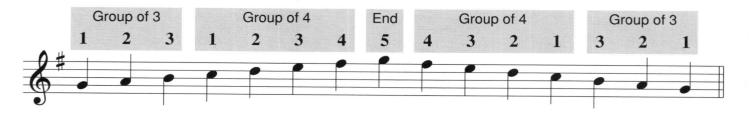

4 The LEFT HAND of G major also uses Pattern 1. Here it is, going down.

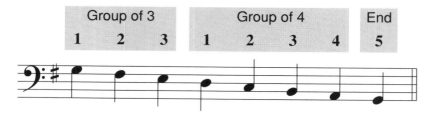

5 Play the left hand of the scale of G major going down, then up.

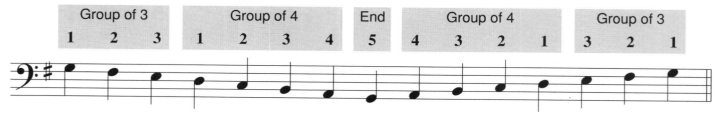

6 Practise the right hand and left hand one-octave scales frequently, until you can play them *from memory* accurately, evenly and rhythmically.

7 Play the right hand scale up and down for two octaves. Notice that the first G is the G below middle C. It will help you to remember that **the fourth finger is only used for F sharp**.

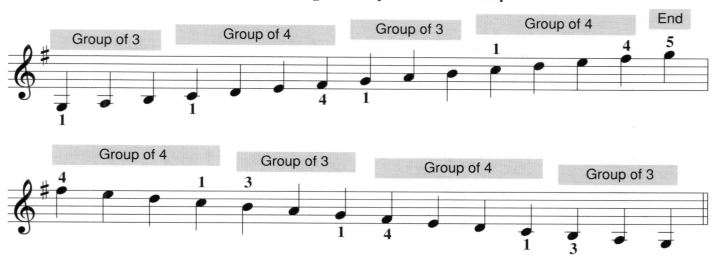

8 Play the two-octave scale of G major in the left hand, going down first and then up. Notice that **the fourth finger is only used for A**.

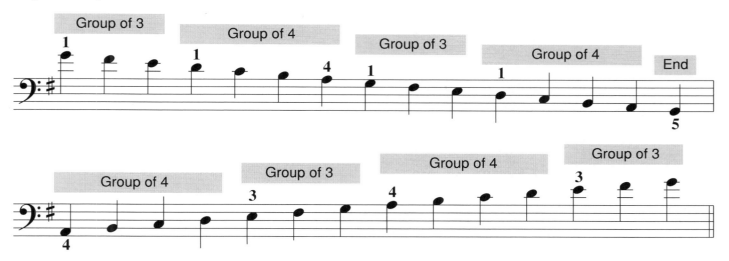

9 Once you can play the scale in paragraph 8 accurately, fluently and evenly, play it going up and then down.

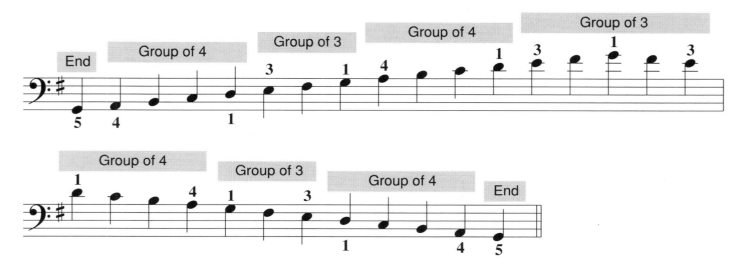

10 When you can play the scales steadily and evenly, try playing them more quickly. In examinations the notes are played as quavers in groups of four.

A suitable tempo to aim for is 60 crotchets per minute, so there are 120 quavers to the minute.

Remember that **all scales must be played from memory**.

G major, right hand

G major, left hand

The Scale of D major

1 The scale of D major is made up of the notes D – E – F *sharp* – G – A – B – C *sharp* and top D.

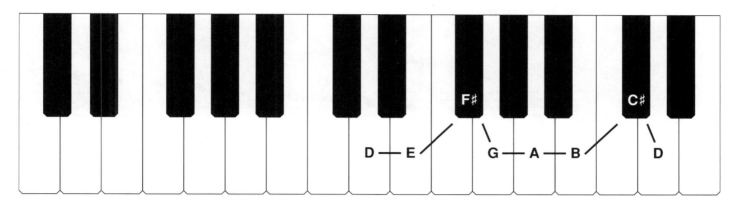

2 Pattern 1 fingering is used for D major. Play the RIGHT HAND going up.

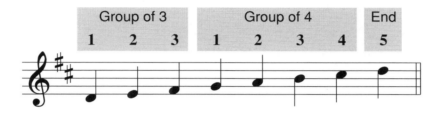

3 Play the right hand of D major going up, then down.

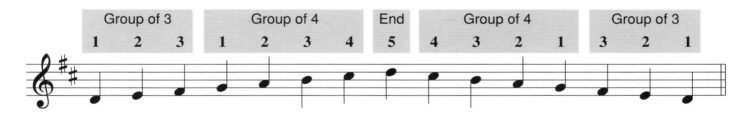

4 The finger pattern for the LEFT HAND is also Pattern 1. Play it, going down.

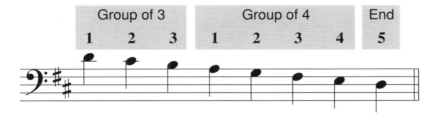

5 Play the scale of D major with the left hand, going down first and then up.

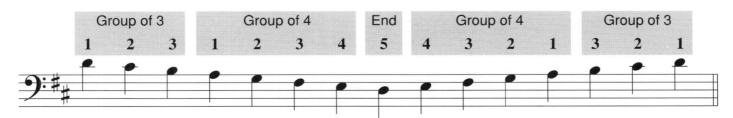

6 Practise the right hand and left hand one-octave scales frequently, until you can play them *from memory* accurately, evenly and rhythmically.

7 Extend the right hand scale up and down for two octaves. It will help you if you remember that the **fourth finger is only used for C sharp**.

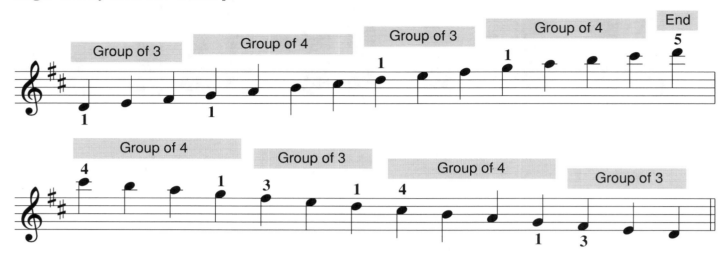

8 Extend the left hand scale to two octaves. Play it down first, then up. Notice that the **fourth finger is used only on E**.

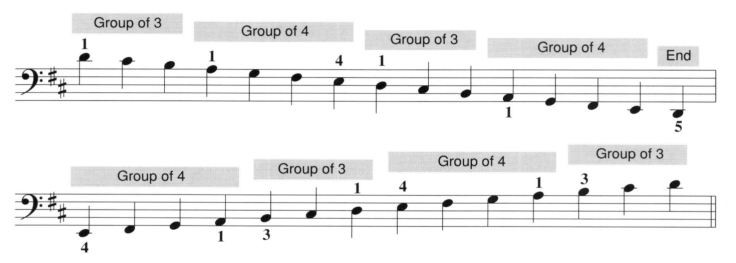

9 Once you can play the scale in paragraph 8 accurately, fluently and evenly, play it up and then down.

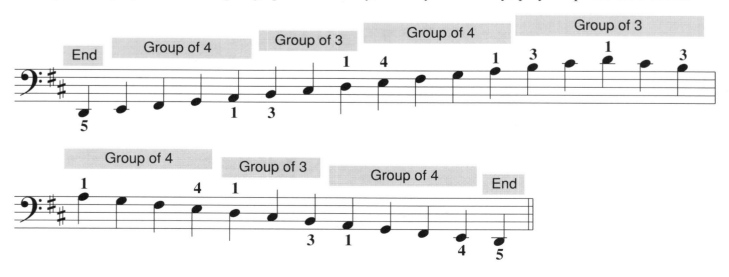

10 When you can play the scales steadily and evenly, try playing them more quickly. In examinations the notes are played as quavers in groups of four.

A suitable tempo to aim for is 60 crotchets per minute, so there are 120 quavers to the minute.

Remember that **all scales must be played from memory**.

The Scale of F major

1   The scale of F major is made up of the notes F – G – A – B *flat* – C – D – E and top F.

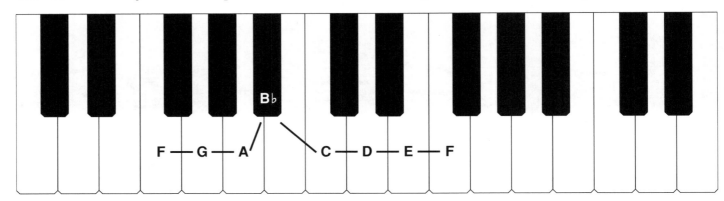

2   The RIGHT HAND of F major **cannot use Pattern 1 fingering**, because its fourth note, B♭, is a black note which cannot easily be played by the thumb. **Pattern 2** fingering is used for the right hand of F major. This starts with a **group of four** notes, fingered 1, 2, 3 and 4, followed by a **group of three** notes fingered 1, 2 and 3. The **end** note, top F, is fingered 4. Play the scale slowly and carefully.

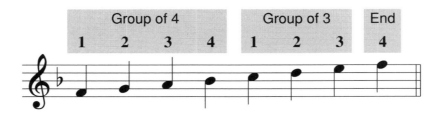

3   Now play the scale of F major with the right hand, going up then down.

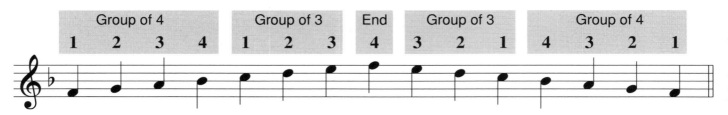

4   The LEFT HAND uses **Pattern 1** fingering. Play it going down first.

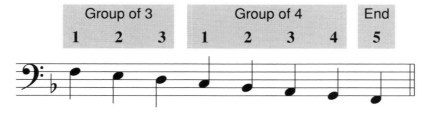

5   Play the scale of F major with the left hand, going down and then up.

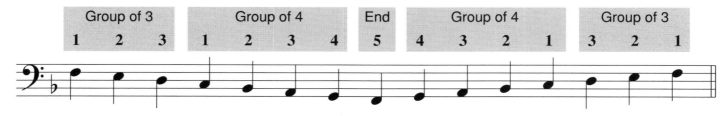

6 Practise the right hand and left hand one-octave scales frequently, until you can play them *from memory* accurately, evenly and rhythmically.

7 Play the right hand scale up and down for two octaves. Notice that the **fourth finger is used for B flat and also for the end note**.

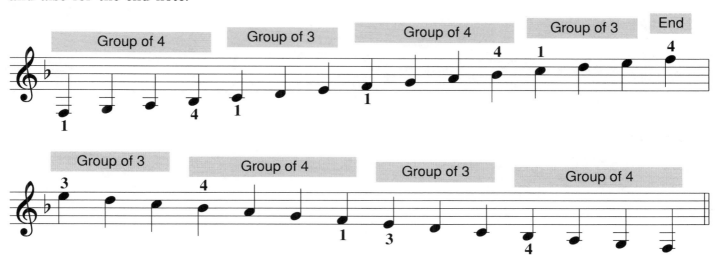

8 Play the left hand scale for two octaves. The scale starts on the F *above* Middle C. Play it downwards first, then up. Notice that **the fourth finger is used only for G**.

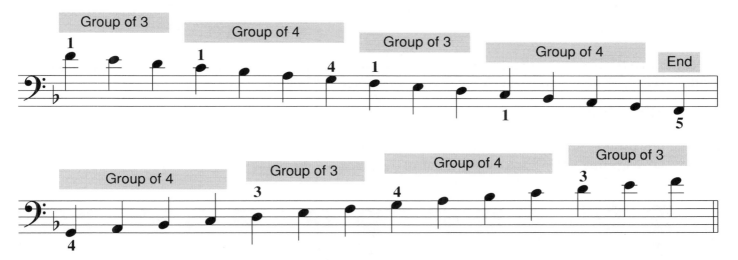

9 Once you can play the scale in paragraph 8 accurately, fluently and evenly, play it upwards first, then down.

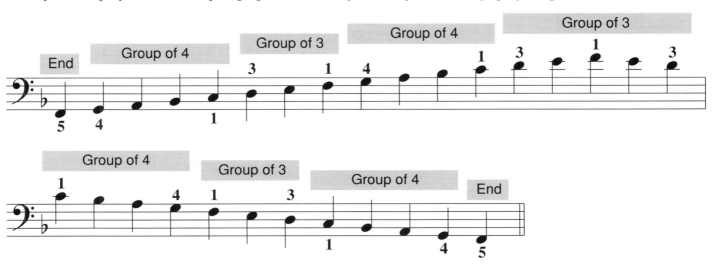

10 When you can play the scales steadily and evenly, try playing them more quickly. In examinations the notes are played as quavers in groups of four.

A suitable tempo to aim for is 60 crotchets per minute, so there are 120 quavers to the minute.

Remember that **all scales must be played from memory**.

F major, right hand

F major, left hand

or

The Scales of A minor

There are two types of minor scale. One is called the **melodic minor**. The other is called the **harmonic minor**. In this grade, you can choose which type you wish to learn. Both are discussed below.

A melodic minor (descending)

1 The downward version of melodic minor scales uses the notes indicated by the scale's key signature. There are no sharp or flats in the key signature of A minor, so the notes in the descending melodic minor scale are A – G – F – E – D – C – B and bottom A.

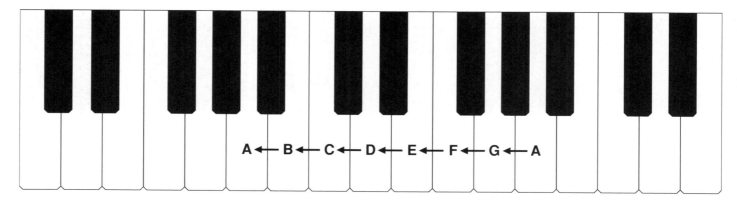

2 Pattern 1 fingering is used for A minor. Play A melodic minor going down first, with the right hand, using the version of Pattern 1 that you learnt for descending scales.

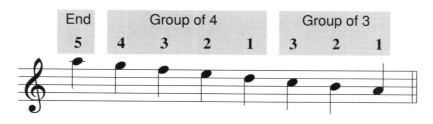

3   Extend the scale to two octaves. Notice that **the fourth finger is used only for G.**

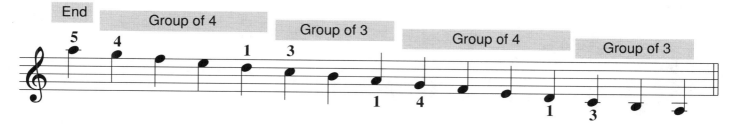

4   Play the left hand descending for one octave.

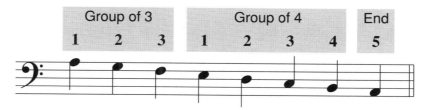

5   Extend the left hand scale to two octaves. Notice that the first note is the A above middle C and that **the fourth finger is used only for B.**

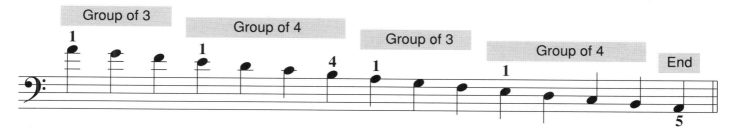

A melodic minor (ascending)

6   When melodic minor scales go up, the sixth and seventh notes of the scale are each raised by a semitone. (Notes are numbered from the bottom upwards). The notes of A melodic minor ascending are therefore A – B –C – D – E – F *sharp* – G *sharp* and top A.

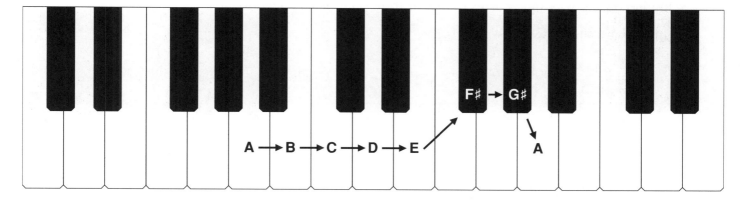

7   With the right hand play the ascending scale of A melodic minor, using Pattern 1 fingering.

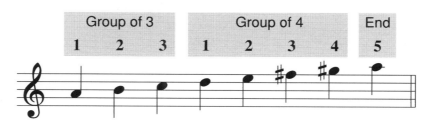

8 Extend the right hand scale to two octaves. Notice that **the fourth finger is used only for G sharp**.

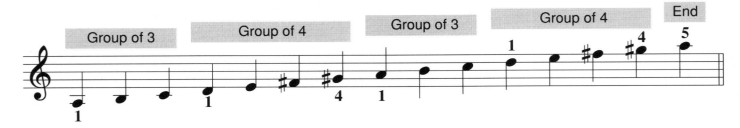

9 Play an octave of the left hand scale going up, using Pattern 1 fingering.

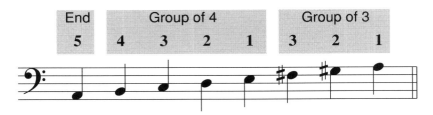

Extend it to two octaves. Notice that **the fourth finger is used only on B**.

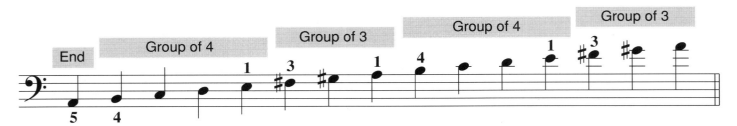

10 Practise the scale of A melodic minor ascending and then descending. Remember to raise notes 6 and 7 by a semitone on the way up, and restore them to normal on the way down.

First play the RIGHT HAND …

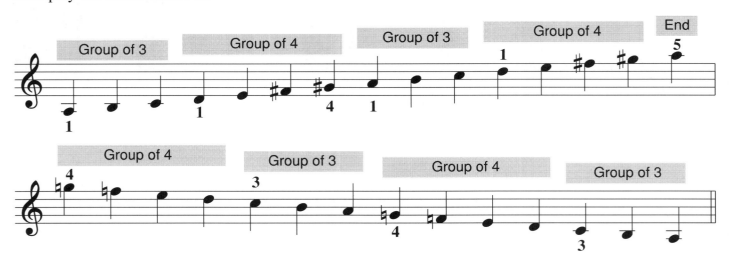

... and then play the LEFT HAND.

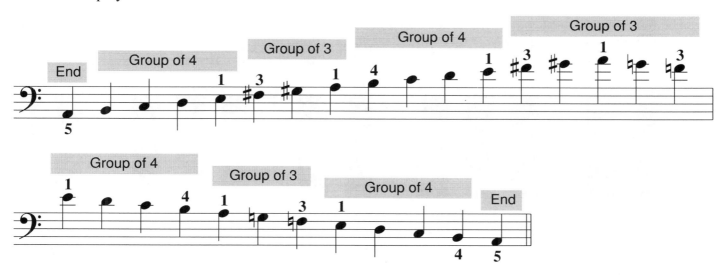

11 When you can play the scales steadily and evenly, try playing them more quickly. In examinations the notes are played as quavers in groups of four.

A suitable tempo to aim for is 60 crotchets per minute, so there are 120 quavers to the minute.

Remember that **all scales must be played from memory**.

A melodic minor, right hand

A melodic minor, left hand

A minor (harmonic)

1 The harmonic form of minor scales goes up and comes down using the notes indicated by its key signature, but with the seventh note *always raised by a semitone*. (Remember that notes are numbered from the lowest note up.) The notes of the A harmonic minor scale are therefore A – B – C – D – E – F – G *sharp* and top A.

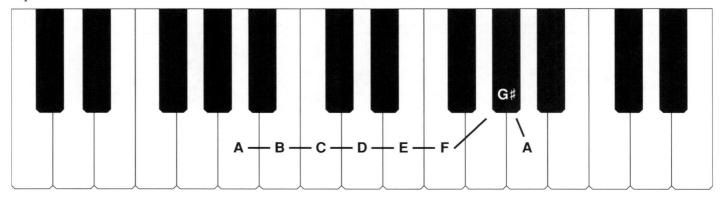

2 The RIGHT HAND goes up and comes down using Pattern 1. Play the ascending scale of A melodic minor.

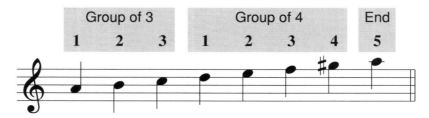

3 Now extend the scale to two octaves. Notice that **the fourth finger is used only for G sharp**.

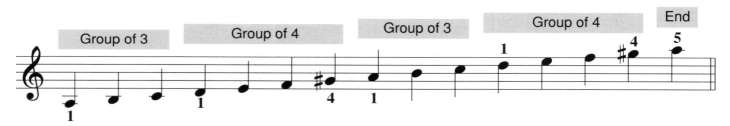

4 Here is one octave of the right hand descending.

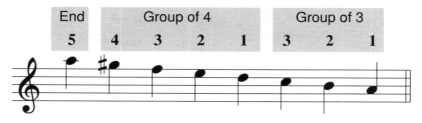

5 Extend the scale to two octaves.

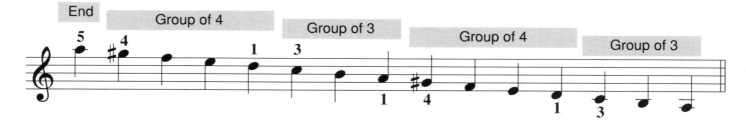

6 The LEFT HAND also uses Pattern 1.

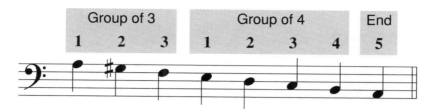

7 Extend the scale to two octaves. **The fourth finger is used only for B.**

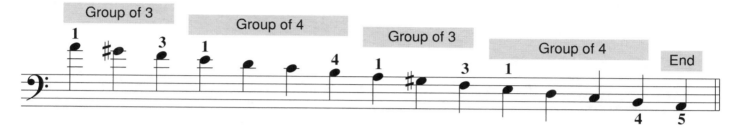

8 Play two octaves of A harmonic minor going up then going down. First in the RIGHT HAND …

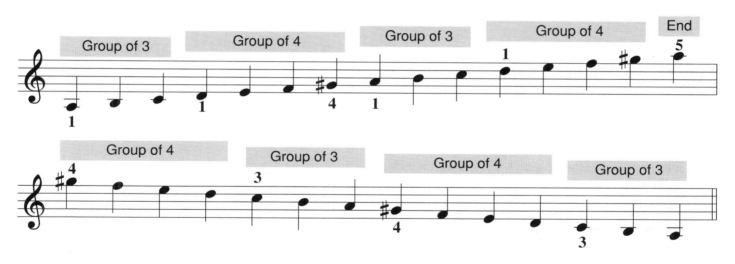

… and then in the LEFT HAND.

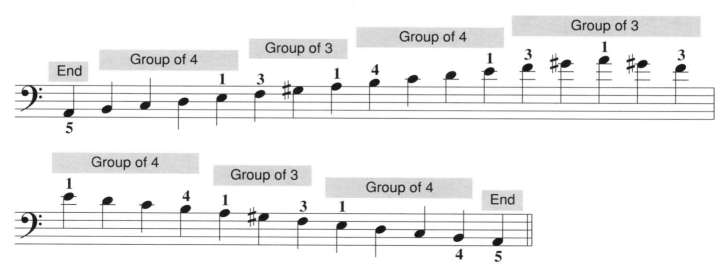

9 When you can play the scales steadily and evenly, try playing them more quickly in groups of four quavers. A suitable tempo to aim for is 60 crotchets per minute, so there are 120 quavers to the minute.

A harmonic minor, right hand

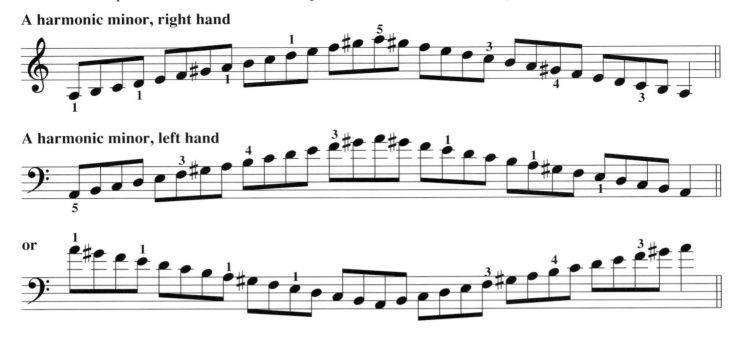

A harmonic minor, left hand

or

The Scales of D minor

In this grade, **you can choose to play EITHER the melodic OR the harmonic scale**. Both are discussed below.

D melodic minor (descending)

1 The downward version of melodic minor scales uses the notes indicated by the scale's key signature. There is a B *flat* in the key signature of D minor, so the notes in the descending melodic minor scale are D – C – B flat – A – G – F – E and bottom D.

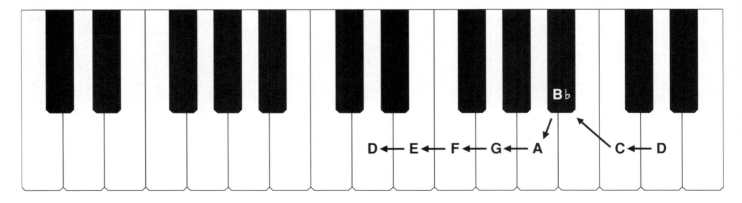

2 The RIGHT HAND comes down using Pattern 1.

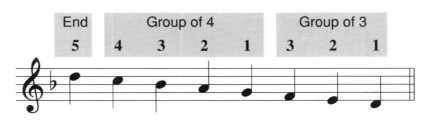

3   Extend the scale to two octaves. Notice that **the fourth finger is used only for C**.

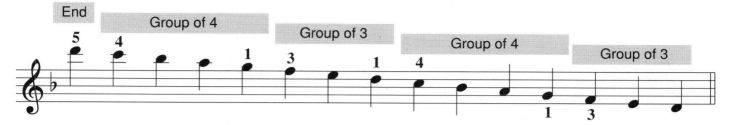

4   Play one octave of the left hand going down.

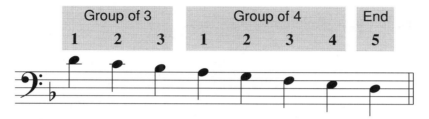

5   Extend this to two octaves. Notice that **the fourth finger is used only for E**.

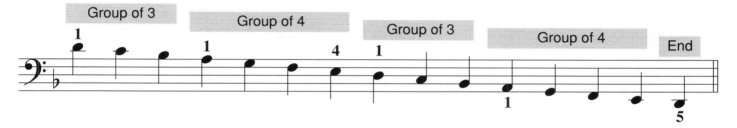

D melodic minor (ascending)

6   When melodic minor scales go up, the sixth and seventh notes of the scale are each raised by a semitone, so the notes of D melodic minor ascending are D – E – F – G – A – B *natural* – C *sharp* and top D.

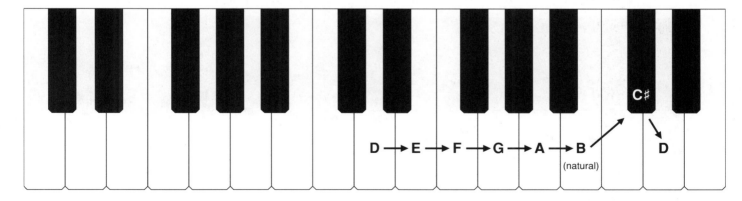

7   With the right hand play the ascending scale of D melodic minor, using Pattern 1 fingering.

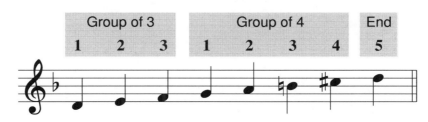

8   Extend the right hand scale to two octaves. Notice that **the fourth finger is used only for C sharp**.

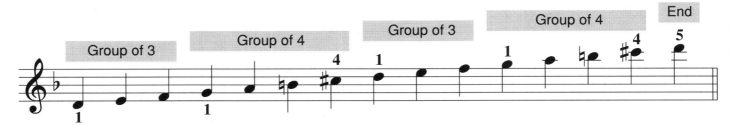

9   Play an octave of the left hand scale going up.

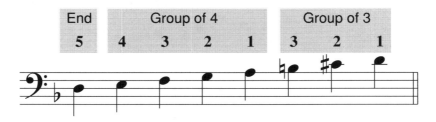

Extend it to two octaves. Notice that **the fourth finger is used only on E**.

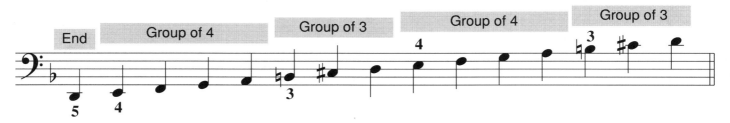

10 Practise the scale of D melodic minor ascending and then descending. Remember to raise notes 6 and 7 by a semitone on the way up, and restore them to normal on the way down.

First play the RIGHT HAND ...

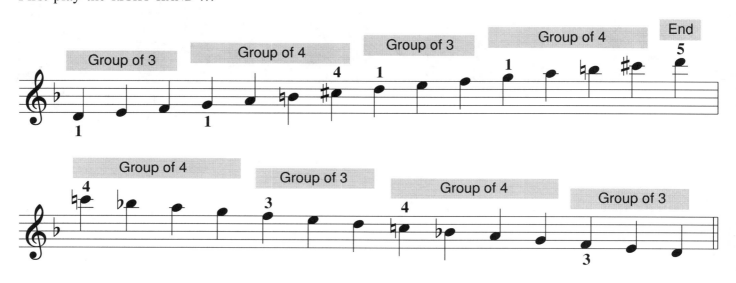

... and then play the LEFT HAND.

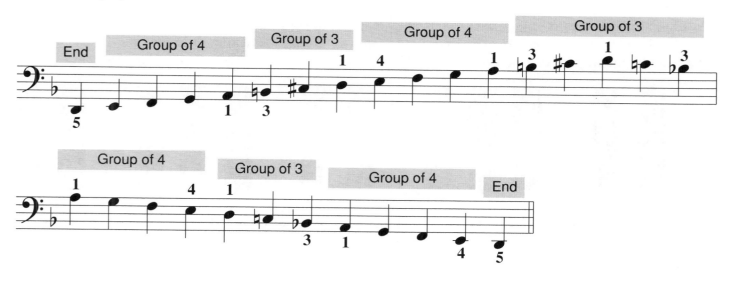

11 When you can play the scales steadily and evenly, try playing them more quickly. In examinations the notes are played as quavers in groups of four.

A suitable tempo to aim for is 60 crotchets per minute, so there are 120 quavers to the minute.

Remember that **all scales must be played from memory**.

D melodic minor, right hand

D melodic minor, left hand

or

D minor (harmonic)

1 The harmonic form of minor scales goes up and comes down using the notes indicated by its key signature, but with the seventh note *always raised by a semitone*. The key signature of D minor is B flat, so the notes of the harmonic minor scale are therefore D – E – F – G – A – B *flat* – C *sharp* and top D.

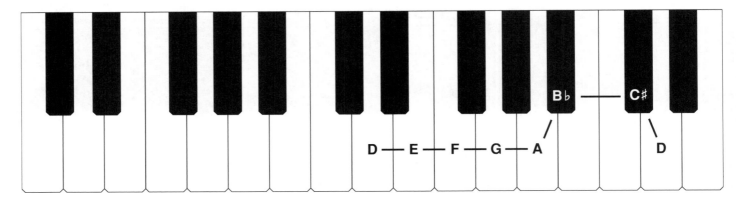

2 The RIGHT HAND goes up and comes down using Pattern 1. Play the ascending scale of D melodic minor. Notice the large gap between B flat and C sharp.

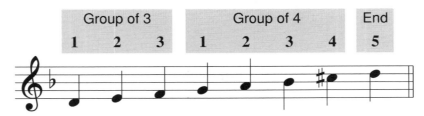

3 Extend the scale to two octaves. Notice that **the fourth finger is used only for C sharp**.

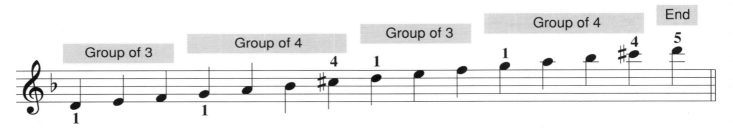

4 Here is one octave of the right hand descending.

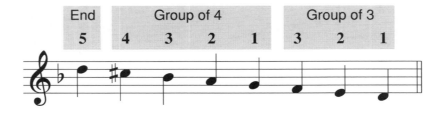

5 Extend the scale to two octaves.

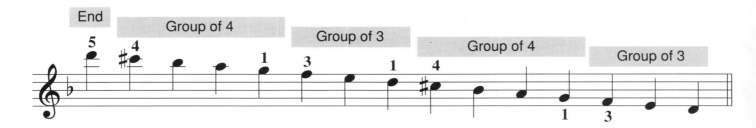

6 The LEFT HAND also uses Pattern 1. Beware of the big gap between C sharp and B flat.

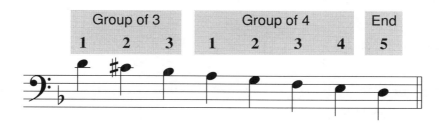

7 Extend the scale to two octaves. **The fourth finger is used only for E.**

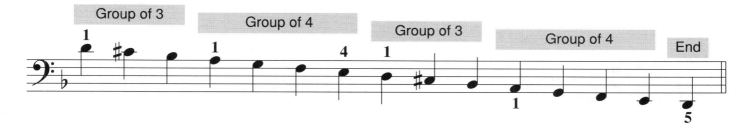

8 Play two octaves of D harmonic minor going up then going down. First in the RIGHT HAND …

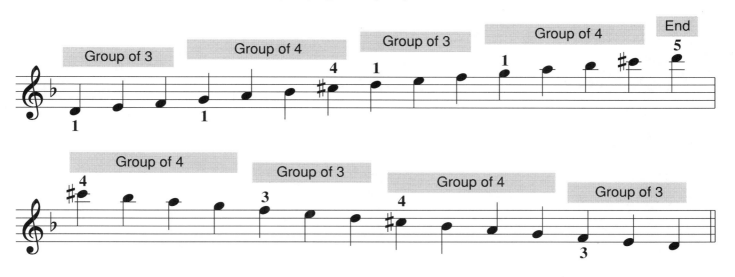

… and then in the LEFT HAND.

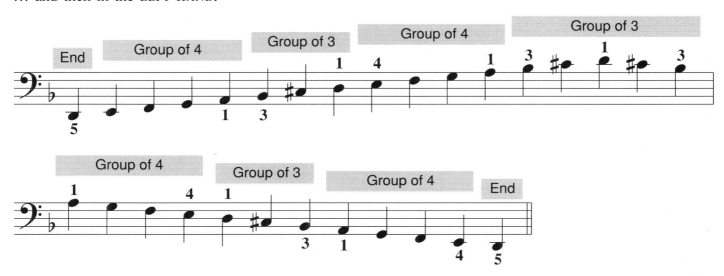

9 When you can play the scales steadily and evenly, try playing them more quickly in groups of four quavers. A suitable tempo to aim for is 60 crotchets per minute, so there are 120 quavers to the minute.

Arpeggios

For Grade 1, arpeggios consist of four notes and can all be fingered in the same way. However, some people prefer to use 3 instead of 4 in the left hand patterns.

C major   The notes are C – E – G and top C.

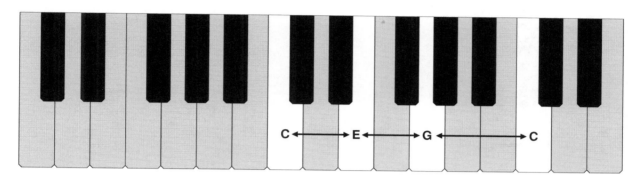

Right hand

Left hand

G major   The notes are G – B – D and top G.

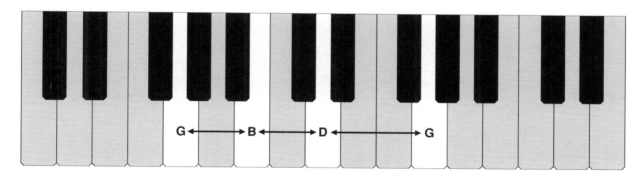

Right hand

Left hand

F major   The notes are F – A – C and top F.

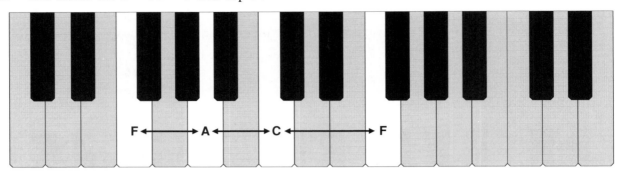

Right hand

Left hand

A minor   The notes are A – C – E and top A.

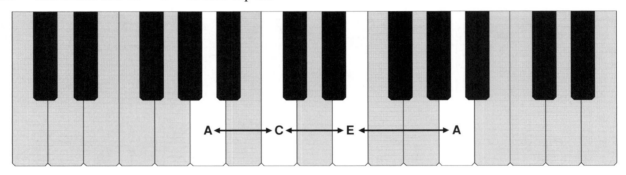

Right hand

Left hand

D minor   The notes are D – F – A and top D.

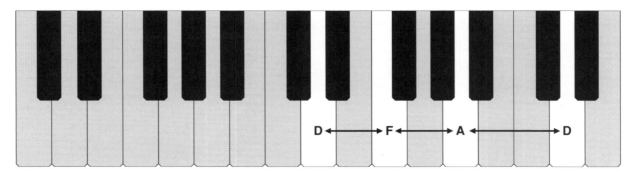

Right hand

Left hand

Broken Chords

1 Broken chords are similar to arpeggios, but their notes are arranged in different patterns. Going up, three groups of three notes are followed by an end note. Going down, the pattern in repeated in reverse, except that the end note is changed.

2 Here is the broken chord of C major. Note that you only need to be able to play each hand separately.

Broken Chord of C major

Right hand

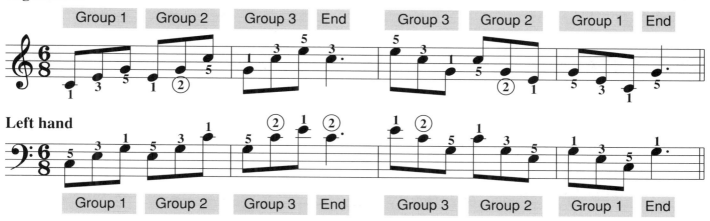

3 You will notice that fingers 1 and 5 are used in *every* group. The middle note of each group is played *usually* with finger 3, but *sometimes* with finger 2.

4 In the RIGHT HAND, Groups 1 and 3 have the middle note played by finger 3. The middle note of Group 2 is played by finger 2.

In the LEFT HAND, Groups 1 and 2 have the middle note played by finger 3. Group 3 has its middle note played by finger 2.

5 Here are the other broken chords you must know for Grade 1. **Fingerings are the same as C major in all of these**, so only markings for finger 2 and the End note are given.

Broken Chord of G major

Right hand

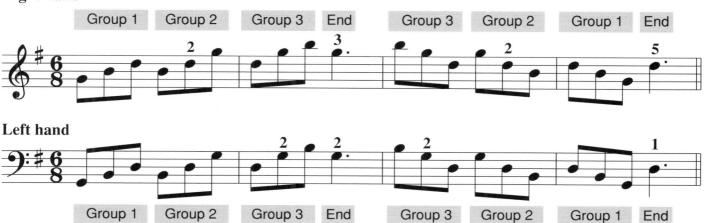

28

Broken Chord of F major

Right hand

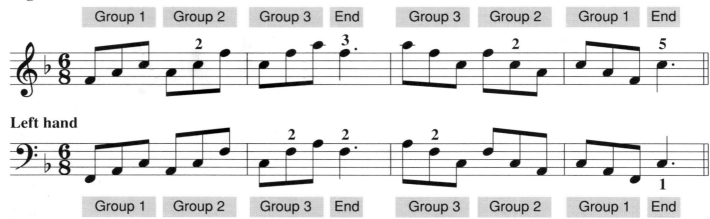

Left hand

Broken Chord of A minor

Right hand

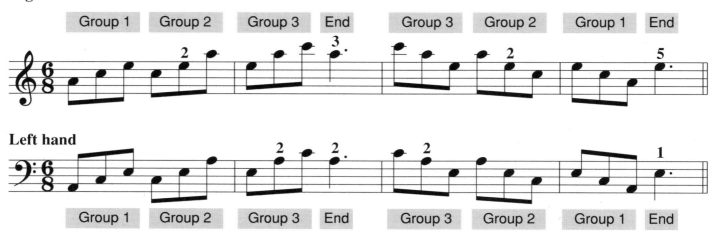

Left hand

Broken Chord of D minor

Right hand

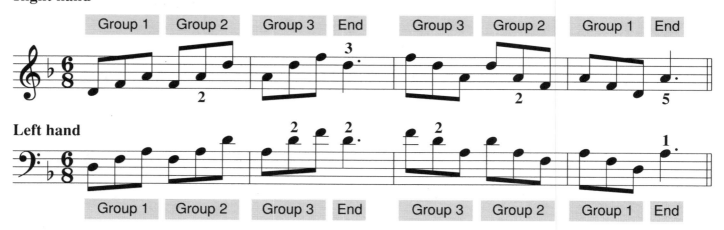

Left hand

Printed by Caligraving Ltd.,
Brunel Way, Thetford, Norfolk. England

1/06 (57502)